THE
GOLDBLUM
VARIATIONS

HELEN
McCLORY

Disclaimer:

The Goldblum Variations is fan-made, unofficial and
unauthorised. It is not affiliated with or endorsed by
the actual Jeff Goldblum in any way.

All Jeff Goldblums in these pages are fictional.

Published by 404 Ink / www.404ink.com / @404ink

ISBN: 9781912489084
ebook: 9781912489091

Printed and bound in Great Britain
by Clays Ltd, St Ives plc

BLACKNESS
Amz | £5.00.
13·11·2018

Contents

A Variety of Jeff Goldblums

The Jeff Goldblum that lathes and sands down a pine table, brushing the grain with the heel of his hand, bends down and takes a spirit level to it, saying gently to the wood, *well done, you.*

☙

The Jeff Goldblum that wakes up in the morning, opens the curtains and says, softly, 'Oh!'

☙

The Jeff Goldblum that, in an excitable mood, makes his maid an origami peacock and leaves it on the top of the fridge (where she, being short, cannot reach it without his helpful boost).

*

The Jeff Goldblum that has never forgotten your birthday, having chanced upon it in the Wikipedia article about you, which he has started to contribute to, although he doesn't really know anything about you at all, and, while his contributions are always peevishly removed by moderators, he is only writing kind and harmless things, like saying your favourite colour is pink, when, citation needed, it might not be so, though it might be, because he, Jeff Goldblum, has surmised a favourability towards pinkness in you, stranger.

*

The Jeff Goldblum that lets tears flow when he dead-heads his roses in winter.

*

The Jeff Goldblum that is reading these stories with his chin in his hands.

The Jeff Goldblum that is reading these stories with his head in his hands.

The Jeff Goldblum that stands in mirth in a frosty walled garden with an armful of   ranunculus he has just set alight.

The Jeff Goldblum that lies awake at night contemplating the creator/the existence of the creator, debating out loud on top of his blankets in lengthy diatribe, or coming to conclusions rapidly, and without a frisson of despair in the least.

The Jeff Goldblum that is a sometimes murderous, sometimes mundane figment in the dream of a woman with aching ankles in Kirkintilloch.

The Jeff Goldblum that rages at the impossibility of opening hard plastic packaging, and, growing increasingly frantic, throws the offender in question (a sealed-shut packet of scissors) across the room, frightening a visiting dog, and leaving him (Jeff Goldblum that is) with a momentary feeling of vertigo at his own emptiness.

The Jeff Goldblum that cannot find his glasses (I think you know where they are).

The Jeff Goldblum that is being the best version of himself.

Jobs for Jeff Goldblum

Firefighter in a ghost town in the desert of Arizona, Jeff Goldblum sits in his bunkroom (one bed, neatly against the wall, a calendar with monthly pictures of Jeff Goldblum in sexy poses, which he did for charity, and also for himself) listening for the alarm to sound, which it has never yet. A brusque wind is lifting the sand outside in thin laces, and at the same time shoving one tumbleweed (that he can see) inexorably around the chain link fence that marks the perimeter of his station.

⁂

Artist in a cold war bunker, Jeff Goldblum is running out of things to sketch and paint. Undeterred, he begins a new project, a recreation of the world itself, as he experiences it: delicately following the lines

5

of the corridors, finding and painting each rivet and scuffmark on the blast walls onto canvas after canvas. He does not think of the world up top. Grey, pink, yellow, grey, grey, grey. There are quite enough colours, even here, and even though he does not know all their names, for him to turn his mind to, to forget.

§

Sprite in a computer game, Jeff Goldblum persists on going against his programming. He is in a battlefield sim, but he has decided he should be much more about gardening, right now. The main part of his army has massed at the foot of the hill and are being charged by the cavalry of the enemy. Jeff Goldblum's apple crop, despite lacking detail, is coming in well this year.

§

Mathematician in a well-regarded university, Jeff Goldblum has written out one (1) formula on the giant whiteboard for his students to copy. Its purpose is unknown to Jeff Goldblum and to his students alike; but look closer, and you will realise swiftly – he has intuited the formula for the perfect tortoise.

Town drunk in a glaciated plateau, Jeff Goldblum tries and fails to get into trouble. The town is forty metres below him, locked in the ice. One must admire his devotion to attempting minor breaches of the peace via graffiti and public urination, here, where there is no public, where there are no longer any buildings worth cherishing.

⁂

Detective in a gated community, Jeff Goldblum expected he would swiftly run out of things to investigate, but has found that there is always plenty of drama, even laying aside all that come from the clichéd notion of residents as prisoners inside the various matryoshka of their days. Consider, as he does, the mystery of the last leaf on the maple tree in front of the concierge's office. When will it fall? Who will take it when it does?

⁂

Clown hitching from habitation to habitation across Russia, Jeff Goldblum is filled with a sense of freedom, but also deep unease. His pockets are full of dusty balloons and lollipops. He keeps hearing bees. Bees, and men yelling. There is never anything around him but the open road and the forest or fields through which one large tractor is slowly charging.

❧

Pubic defence lawyer in small unnamed country, Jeff Goldblum is unfamiliar with not only statute and case law but also with the basic practice of being a lawyer. He is trying his best to provide adequate representation for those who cannot afford to secure a lawyer themselves. Mostly, the people of the courtroom are pleased to see him, a celebrity. Quite often there is undue noise. One day, a joyous fight broke out between a witness for the prosecution and a juror. Jeff Goldblum resolved this by signing *both* of their stomachs in his blood, allowing proceedings to continue.

❧

Writer of short absurdist fiction, Jeff Goldblum – no, I cannot. I should just stop it here. Look, I'm already getting dizzy. Dizzy and sick. I am thinking too much of his fingers typing through and over my own, sliding into the space where my joints are (although, being longer, the fit is not correct and we hit the keys at a delay from one another). Oh, no, this is just wrong. I apologise for ever beginning on this path.

Cooking with Jeff Goldblum

Announcer: Good evening and welcome to another *Cooking with Jeff Goldblum*, or rather, hello for the first and final time. It's midnight, the clocks are all asleep, and we're... *Cooking with Jeff Goldblum*! Now give a warm 'witching hour' hiss to the man himself... Jeff Goldblum!

Jeff Goldblum (*enters and crosses the room in big lanky strides until he reaches the cooking space. Pushes his glasses up his nose, smiles, puts his hand on the wooden counter, takes in the audience and the noise of their hissing and cheers*): ...

Announcer: So, Jeff Goldblum, what are you preparing for us tonight? We're all hungry. We're all waiting. I have my bib on. I love you.

Jeff Goldblum (*pulls up a basket from under the counter. An overhead camera shows the audience that the basket is full of mushrooms, homely, white and brown things with little flecks of dirt on their warm-looking nubs and gills*): …

Announcer: Wow! Look at those lads!

Jeff Goldblum (*pulls up a large stock pot and puts it on the stovetop then shows the audience inside his sleeve. There is nothing. He shows the other sleeve. Nothing. He waves his hands and claps – suddenly he is holding a peeled shallot. He begins chopping this on the counter. He minces it very finely and puts it in the stock pot. He lights the flame under the stock pot and sweats the shallot. Then he produces a jug of vegetable stock*): …

Announcer: Is that vegetable stock? Nice. Can't have soup without a liquid, I always say. It can be any liquid. If you have any liquid, you have imminent soup.

Jeff Goldblum (*pours the vegetable stock over the sweated shallot and adds a bay leaf and some cracked pepper. He begins to chop up the mushrooms. An overhead camera shows his hands holding the mushrooms carefully. He chops each mushroom with consideration of its size and form, so that the resulting pieces are more or less the same size*): …

Announcer: Battle to the death!

Jeff Goldblum (*turns down the flame under the stock pot and adds the mushrooms by great handfuls. He stirs the mixture. The quantity of mushroom is greater than the quantity of stock. Once the stirring is done, he puts a lid on the stock pot and stands in a pose. This pose changes slowly over the course of ~25 minutes as Jeff Goldblum mimics Michelangelo's David, Rodin's The Thinker, a generic version of Herakles, several Moore sculptures, a Giacometti and, with a startling chrome finish, Koon's Rabbit*): ...

Announcer: Looks like that soup's ready. We're hungry, Jeff Goldblum.

Jeff Goldblum (*nods, takes a ladle and begins stirring the soup. He pulls out the bay leaf and discards it. He opens a brandy bottle and tips a little in. Then produces a stick blender, blending the soup to a creamy finish. A pair of black opera-gloved hands reach over across the stage, far longer than the span of a human arm, and hand him a stack of bowls. He begins ladling the soup into the bowls*): ...

Announcer: Yes. Salvation is here, folks.

Jeff Goldblum (*carries bowls on a large tray out into the audience. The camera pans round. The studio is full of all kinds of strange figures; some like blue-grey vapour with eyes, others harried looking men from early 18th century comics, a stick figure, still more contemporary humans in jeans and tee-shirts that say 'Cooking with Jeff Goldblum… and me!' on them. Everyone takes a bowl. Even the person who appears to be a mushroom – they eat heartiest of all. Jeff goes back to the stage with two bowls. He looks up*): …

Announcer: What is this? What is this?

Jeff Goldblum (*still looking up, beckons*): …

Announcer (*descends from the ceiling, a creature of gold and whalebone corsetry*): …

Jeff Goldblum (*waits until the announcer has a spoon and bowl in hand, then picks up his own bowl and begins to drink from it directly and purpose*): … shhlll

Announcer (*begins soup, finishes soup, places the bowl back down, and in a voice both similar to and remote from the voice they had used earlier, spun with strange threads of intent, addresses the camera*): And that's all of Jeff Goldblum for tonight. Now back to our regular programming.

This was not a test. When the bell chimes, please leave your home through the front door, making sure to help anyone in the household who needs assistance, but leaving any bags and shoes behind. Thank you. God speed!

Jeff Goldblum (*waves, smiling, steps back into a pool of darkness*): …

Big Mood with Jeff Goldblum

Louche, in a shopping trolley, legs adangle, fore-arms at rest on the metal rim, in an empty megastore at midnight, being pushed up and down the aisles by a pair of twins (adult, male) who have not fully real-ised who they are pushing about, since, on their part, certain substances have been recently inhaled (glitter, new-born star-matter).

☙

Pensive, in a DMV (department of motor vehicles) office, thumbing through the dollar bills in his wallet, sure he has forgotten something, while a small fire is roiling in a waste paper bin behind the counter, send-ing up a reed of smoke.

❦

Joyous, in the cathedral of light that is the forest on a spring day, green light and beams, bluebells, bird-song, oh, and trembling susurrations in the canopy, he goes roaming on his long legs like a cryptid and the sight of him, a mere glimpse, brings gladness to the hearts of ramblers, and they in their part will never raise their phones or their cameras to record his passing, so as not to pierce the air of precious calmness this vision has laid down upon their hearts.

❦

Irrepressible, in a room full of dust – a ballroom in a formerly sealed up castle in France, untouched since the war – as he walks up to the mantelpiece (precise footsteps, watching them make their mark in the years' grey sediment) (a wide floor, a few sad velveteen chairs and end tables with empty champagne glasses perched on them, a window out onto the decrepit estate) to stare a moment in the tarnished mirror (gilding, scrolls of ivy and grapes), slowly a smile breaking over his face, as he puts his head down lips first on the surface of the mantelpiece and goes 'bllllrrrrrppp', blowing rolls of dust away, getting dust on his nose, which he claps off with one quick hand, turns, and chugs away through the room, kicking up as much dust as he can on the way out (with a giggle? Yes, if you'd like, a giggle).

※

Desperate, in a white, denuded landscape, checking his watch as the horizon begins to close down on him, as day begins to get lightheaded and the sounds of whispers take up in the reeds beside the river (he is walking by a river, he thinks it is a river, but it could also be the long train of a dress).

※

Lusty, at the top of a mountain, wearing goat legs, throwing his arms up, up, as a huge spring tide full of fishes and catastrophe splashes over the world.

※

Sympathetic, as he sits alone in a theatre watching a play on its opening night (he knows, its only night), a play about a man who has been all things to everyone but has also been trapped in a painting for many years unable to, as he very much would like, wink at his favourite occupant of the house (a charming but lonely individual called Firdy who always wears gloves and communicates in warbles).

⁂

Severe, as he addresses an audience at a university graduation ceremony, telling them, each, individually, of the futures they can expect for themselves, not sparing any detail of a sorrow or wrenching moment of self-abasement, and granting each graduand, after telling them their fates before everyone, there in the graduating hall, a tight dry hug and a respectful nod.

⁂

Restless, as with tears in his eyes he stands at the racetrack willing an errant fly (which has been caught up in the tumble of the horses) to be the first across the line, poor little beast, though he knows as soon as the race is over he must run, even before collecting his winnings (if indeed the fly wins) to catch the train waiting to take him onwards through the blue snows of a vast, impersonal northern country.

Boorish, sitting on the steps outside a chip shop in the drizzle, pummelling fistfuls of chips into his mouth, watching people go by on their business (such as it might be at two in the am), occasionally throwing chips in the hopes that one person or another will catch one and spin on their feet, and yell back 'You've no idea, Jeff Goldblum, how glad I am I passed you by!'

Checking in on Jeff Goldblums
on Alternative Earths

In this universe, Jeff Goldblum is a folded corduroy jacket (pale pink) on a shelf in your wardrobe. Oh happy day!

♣

On this version of our Earth, there is no sun (no stars anywhere), and hence no life. We could pretend that this rock is Jeff Goldblum, but why contribute to making the world appear to our temporary vision that more the tragic?

♣

This is the Earth where everything is two-dimensional and made of paper. Here is Jeff Goldblum, line-drawn pilot to a folded plane, flying from the hand of a line-drawn child. Soon he will be crumpled up and tossed on a paper fire, which, being paper, never consumes all of its fuel (or oxygen, or heat), and so he will burn (such as he can be said to) in their whickering flames till the end of days come.

※

On this Earth, Jeff Goldblum is almost entirely as he is on our Earth, except that his arms have been permanently coated in gold (it is the style here, but he started it).

※

Here, Jeff Goldblum is a ghost. In this universe, ghosts are demonstrably real, as are mermaids, dragons, selkies, bigfoot, vampires, werewolves, the Sidhe, universal human rights, you, the things you touch and taste, doppelgangers, decent harassment-free parts for women in Hollywood pictures, mint ice cream that actually tastes like mint, the angels (God is still outwith easy provability), the transformative darkness of Hallowe'en, and your dreams. No one lives past the age of forty-four.

❧

On this Earth, the dinosaurs never died out. Giving it a cursory look, Jeff Goldblum isn't here. No, I don't think a dinosaur version of him is here either.

❧

In this universe, you are Jeff Goldblum, and I am uncomfortable, but all is, and has been, and will be, well.

❧

Here, there is no here. There is only the great eye and the motes in it which are our sanctuary and our torment, and the sweeping lashes there above as below, and the cathedral of the pupil who swellest as the light and as the dark decrees, and the colour of the iris is unknown, and we must not ask, and we are the matter of the eye, and unmade in moments, remade, unmade – (all right, in all likelihood, it is Jeff Goldblum's eye).

The universe of [redacted beverage]™, a kind of bubble-bestrewn red-brown hell that you will create in your own way in imagining it. Jeff Goldblum would never be here.

This Earth sees Jeff Goldblum making choices he did not make in our world. I see him lying in a hammock, looking very content. I'm sure he's just as content in our reality, sometimes, just as he may be discontent or harried in this, at another time, when we are not observing him. Rest easy, Jeff Goldblum, whatever your life in this place may be.

In this universe, our moon (alone of all moons) has seasons. Now, it's Autumn, and the moon is a rust colour, shedding parts of itself. The moon falls in flakes on Jeff Goldblum's shoulders and on the floor of the meadow in which he stalks. You would not know him to see him. He looks over at us, says, *do not be afraid*, but we can be nothing else.

※

In this reality, it's too windy. Jeff Goldblum has an oversized high-neck Aran jumper on. Oh, wait. I think he has grown it, like a fur, to cover himself in the nippy air. He looks cosy, ay?

※

This is the Earth where love is parcelled out by governments on a supposed meritocracy, though in practice the rich receive far more than is fair. Jeff Goldblum is writing a letter on a balcony in Buenos Aires. His face with all its well-earned lines is placid. His portion of love, for the time, remains unobservable.

※

This is the alternative Earth where every shameful feeling you have ever had congregates around you like a barbed scarf. Oh. OH.

※

This is our final alternative Earth, so please enjoy it as much as you can, with that edge of poignancy the last of all things gives to us. Jeff Goldblum is a small boy here, for this world is slightly out of sync with ours. He doesn't know who he will be yet, and neither do we, from one moment to another; he can be Jeff Goldblum, or Jeff Goldblum. There is dirt under his nails. He has been playing in the yard. The sky here is violet by the way, and every smell reminds you, almost, of a scent you last breathed in when your life was much different to how it is now. This is the world you can choose to stay in. Hold up your hand. If you join, it will be an old century for a good long time, though events that happened in our world may not happen here, or not in the same order. This is your choice. In this alternative Earth, this is a choice you can make. What is absurd about this is only that (in our actual world, in which you are reading this) you do not have a choice to stay or not to stay.

I envy and do not envy you.

[ ] ments of [ ] eff Goldbl[ ]
(fragments)

I first saw Jeff Goldblum in the 1995 (I think) ▇▇▇▇▇▇▇▇▇▇. I liked that he always wore black and had a knowing cocky manner that ▇▇▇▇ ▇▇▇ endearing – I know now as a grown up how hard ▇▇▇ a kind of male certainty (▇▇▇▇) without the malingering ▇▇▇▇▇▇▇▇▇k. ▇▇▇▇▇▇▇▇▇▇▇ Fly I saw him perturbed ▇▇▇ the (sloppiness of) the body under technical pressures. He was ▇▇▇▇▇ quite unexpectedly and I don't think since. It was one with Diane Keaton. Who ▇▇▇ though? The shining ▇▇▇▇▇▇▇▇▇ Hotel was Jeff Goldblum's small role as ▇▇▇ – still one of the greatest representations of ▇▇▇ on screen in my limited experience ▇▇▇▇▇▇▇ nails that quiet dedicated ▇▇▇ the way they have to explain ▇▇▇

and sometimes do so in the most words possible to facilitate the █████ under█████ I have absolutely ██████████████ Jeff Goldblum as a man. I don't think I've ever seen an interview with him? So why █████ this book ██████████Ah perhaps it goes back ██████████████ whatever it was. He dripped water ██████████ Dern's wrist. He was wounded but still clever. ██████████████████ t desire, not objectification, not even a connection ██████████ though I still don't ██████████████ sometimes words are not the issue but █ frail transfer from feeling to words, in which █ falls and █ to cross into concrete and ~~██████~~ terms.

❧

Jeff Goldblum [ ] gmented in my [ ] pre[ ]tion of [ ]

[ ] like to know yourself as much [ ] a figment of a celebrity

In memes **Jeff Goldblum** [ ] talk[ ] out gen [ ] loved marvel [ ] ers

But there is never any way to [ ]

When I look at glasses of water I

[ ] chaos

[ ] which is a pretty remarkable thing.

❧

(text fed through Google Translate –
English-Catalan-English-Cantonese-English)

Jeff GOLDBLUM on the chair! Jeff Goldblum In
the rainbow of the rainbow, JUMPER is a well-de-
served person you do not know seems to be a good
man! Jeff Goldblon Jeff Goldblum do not know me,
hope he does not ask! Jeff Gederbrom to deceive the
translation and translation of the forest! I hope that a
woman in Scotland is scarcity and is trying to under-
stand a man in Hollywood, she is a woman who is
not familiar with her career, that man is famous for
her career, but even what is known for his personality
None of them, if Jeff Goldblum is writing this book,
it might be more powerful. Or you.

❧

...I've seen the tunnel at the end

        of the fallen oak, I've followed

with my eyes the frames

      frames

      frames

      of a single hopping bird until it disappeared, I've :

           slept out.

I've been rough. I've held a cup with both hands for pleasure.   I've forgotten what a genuine human pair of

                                  eyes look like I've clocked spines. This is a

                            I've got lost in the ligature of your left hand. This is a

poem that intends to portray.   Like a film intends to portray, or elides, or evades or rolls over

like a heft animal dying.   Like an actor this poem is very careful, an instinctive, and lost.

Like an island this poem is lost.   Like a poem this poem is following you in a gesture of

praise in a gesture of frank dismay.   Like words meant to be rerad out this poem is an

engine whose oak is sapped without a body in minute and grander motion.

      Like molten latext for a

special effect this poem is solely in your hands. And perhaps dripping

                                over them into...

Jeff Goldblum on Jeff Goldblum (randomised and trimmed – text taken from GQ)

The flower goes up and poetic and that having a kid makes younger. I feel younger. I like anybody, but one of the best withers, and you're Not an Apple, Man. Put me in from nature and be part of a raging bull and that's all looks. Luckily it's still mostly the world's you live.

Try to be you feel—what seems best with the best with whom younger. The Best Medicine Is Contemplate the Wonders of the cosmos and certainly educational in it. The Best Medicine Is Contemplating nature—and down. Then I go side to say. That'll probably keep your time. The fleeting a kid makes your head on straight. With an infant son and vegetables and what I'd had plastic surgery. I things that if I lose my hair, I'll crap my pants like I'm excited by the ageing process.

I think I'm plenty buzzy. I'm plenty buzzy. I'm plenty buzzy as a horse. I do chest presses with the stuff. I'm not fighting that now. Don't smoke. We know about that make me buzzy.

Jeff Goldblum Bingo
(Bingo Goldbingo)

Jeff Goldblum in Independence Day (1996)	Jeff Goldblum in Earth Girls are Easy (1988)	Jeff Goldblum in Augie Rose (2000)	Jeff Goldblum in Powder (1995)	Jeff Goldblum in Into the Night (1985)
Jeff Goldblum in Fay Grim (2006)	Jeff Goldblum in The Big Chill (1983)	Jeff Goldblum in Spinning Boris (2003)	Jeff Goldblum in Deep Cover (1992)	Jeff Goldblum in The Adventures of Buckaroo Banzai across the 8th Dimension (1984)
Jeff Goldblum in The Grand Budapest Hotel (2014)	Jeff Goldblum in Cats & Dogs (2001)	★	Jeff Goldblum in The Favour, The Watch and the Very Big Fish (1991)	Jeff Goldblum in Thor: Ragnarok (2017)
Jeff Goldblum in Invasion of the Body Snatchers (1978)	Jeff Goldblum in The Player (1992)	Jeff Goldblum in Igby Goes Down (2002)	Jeff Goldblum in The Fly (1986)	Jeff Goldblum in Chain of Fools (2000)
Jeff Goldblum in Pittsburgh (2006)	Jeff Goldblum in Jurassic Park (1993)	Jeff Goldblum in Adam Resurrected (2008)	Jeff Goldblum in Morning Glory (2010)	Jeff Goldblum in Between the Lines (1977)

How to play Bingo Goldbingo

Gather your friends. Give them each a copy of Bingo Goldbingo (buy them a copy of this book, print out a larger version from http://www.404ink.com/bingo-goldbingo, or do it by hand if you have that kind of time and love for such an intimate work). Sit in a good space. Choose one person to be Jeff Goldblum and have 'him' yell out titles of 'his' movies in random order (randomise using the traditional balls printed with Jeff Goldblum's films on them, or trust that your 'Jeff Goldblum' has a commitment to the random and will not read out each more than once). If a player has seen the movie, they can mark it off the list. The first person to mark off a complete row of Jeff Goldblum roles wins.

Appropriate prizes

A wink

Oh, the stars

Bath full of glitter

DVD box set (empty)

Tickets to Jeff Goldblum

A book of blighted affirmations

Partially used paint pots (sample sized)

Today I wrote Nothing by Daniil Kharms

Life-sized cut out of Jeff Goldblum as Dr Ian Malcolm

All the flowers in a neighbour's garden (ask permission)

A drawing by me (please be aware I cannot draw very well)

Gentle kiss from the last, aging resident of a Parisian apartment building

Your da

The mire

A high five

Teddy Bear pyramid constructed as their tomb

Satisfaction and general acclaim

A photograph of a rainbow over a phone box

A nice jacket or handful of fresh straw

Jeff Goldblum without Spellcheck

(handwritten)

When I think of Jeff Goldblum, I think of sly roles, rainbow jumpers (I mean all kinds of colours of thread not just rainbows), I suppose I think 'f things that are not 'Jeff Goldblum but adjacent in my mind eg/ Jeffs I have known, jungles of ferns (the mind just ricochets from suggestion to subliminal to something of comfort.)

I think : glisten, I think : chocolatey — brown, footsteps (one imagines the footsteps of celebrities are more definitive, crisper, more 'footfall-y' than those of a regular persons).

I think a lot of Jeff Goldblum as a fiction and from there to fictional people I have made in the past, a through (a comfort + a worry (at once) that in a parallel universe all these fictions (daydreams, characters, half-ideas) are real + sometimes, just slightly, they remember me, & the readers who bear them aloft in their minds, even only once.

Past lives of Jeff Goldblum

Eighty years ago, in the long undergrowth in some part of North America – it is hard to guess where, this close up – a grass snake wends along, drawn by the squeaks of a blind newly-born mouse that has somehow wriggled from its nest. It smells like a good meal to the snake. If you were to gently peel back the grasses through which the grass snake passes, you would see its dark body moving fast and with a sense of purpose you can only envy. This is Jeff Goldblum, grass snake.

❦

In the court of the Medici, a man is reading out from a notice about a new type of fruit discovered in the Americas. Lorenzo de Medici has just recently died, murdered in Venice by two hired killers. However, there is no mourning when the first batch of this new edible, 'the tomato', arrives in the Medici kitchens. The cook is the first person in perhaps all of Firenze to brave a bite out of the soft red flesh. He spits it out in disgust. It is mealy and full of slimy seeds. He declares he will make it for the devils upstairs, since it is so fit for their character. Somehow, he is not reported, and goes on to live a long, full life. Jeff Goldblum, in this form, never grows to like tomatoes.

Once a woman, the cleverest in her village, left behind all she knew to travel to the city (the first city, at least, the longest continually inhabited in all this world). She walked under the palms, driving a donkey in front of her. In Jericho she became a maid to a rich woman, who loved her. Dearly, the days passed her, and she loved each one, until the day her mistress died. Then she walked to the river, and threw herself in. Strangely, she did not sink, nor did any water go in her lungs. She was carried down the Jordan all the way to the Dead Sea, where she – Jeff Goldblum in this life – was quite out of the danger of sinking, and so got out, and resolved to start again. Strange, yes, but such things could happen then, in the very early days of our era.

☙

A bird, a bird, before there were words you would recognise for birds, only the cry, come from below, of someone who, on the cusp of speech, wants to say how it is to see that bird sling itself across the bright, crystalline, pre-civilisation air.

☙

For many years a bacterial colony, asexually recreating itself over and over again, brimming with inventive-ness, until it cannot quite be said that it was the same being (Jeff Goldblum) it was in the very beginning, nor quite yet that it has evolved into anything new, and the years it took to do this are a little beyond us right now, being not on an easy, human scale, as most of the universe is not.

Jeff Goldblum,
The Final Variations

Jeff Goldblum siting in his study awkwardly Googling HOW ARE CAPYBARAS SO CHILLED OUT? in all caps, even though he already knows the answer.

🌿

Jeff Goldblum wiping his face with a heavy gilded washcloth designed (so the packaging says) with 18 carat gold scientifically proven to 'obliterate' even the finest wrinkles.

🌿

Jeff Goldblum concentrating hard while making a gruyere soufflé and rocket salad for a friend who isn't particularly hungry or fond of cheese but is too polite to say.

$$\maltese$$

Jeff Goldblum considering a script while sitting upside down on his stairs, with his head towards the foot of the stairs and his legs towards the top of the stairs and an iced coffee somewhere behind him in danger of being spilt.

$$\maltese$$

Jeff Goldblum walking shoeless into a house made of cats; just cats for walls, cats for soft (very soft) furnishings, cats making up the window frame for a view outside of the garden of cats (flowering) and tall deciduous cat trees. In a gently-purring room upstairs Jeff Goldblum inspects a painting (which is a cat) of a cat, which has been propped up against the bed (made of several cats resting peacefully in the late afternoon sun). It would be cruel to hang that painting up, to have to nail it to the wall, he thinks. It's good that it's on the floor.

Jeff Goldblum walking down a long street in a coastal settlement in Delaware, unsure of the name of this place, since he has only just stopped on a whim, possibly to investigate a boat that is for sale (although he doesn't need a boat right now).

※

Jeff Goldblum singing a lullaby to a room full of newborn babies, none of whom will remember this performance, not in any graspable way, but nevertheless, he thinks, it's good for them to have heard a lullaby, to be unified in this fashion, just hours out of the womb.

※

Jeff Goldblum standing in a laundrette with a pleasant lack of narrative drive in this story.

※

Jeff Goldblum in a Santa beard, throwing bricks at a woollen mill shop.

§

Jeff Goldblum practicing how to laugh backwards in a very large and empty auditorium situated on the outskirts of Medicine Hat, Alberta.

§

Jeff Goldblum picking strawberries for himself from a pick-your-own strawberry farm, staring intently at each fruit as it spins between his finger and thumb by a green stalk, though mostly thinking nothing, about the negative space between strawberries as his punnet is filled, and then about the texture of strawberries as he bites into them, carving at them with his teeth until there is nothing left but the tops, resembling very small plants of their own, and which he tosses into the field, figuring anything organic returns to the soil just fine, better there than trapped pocket of sullied air in a landfill far away from their point of origin.

＊

Jeff Goldblum picking his nose – but we're going to look away now, for mercy. Here's Jeff Goldblum standing in front of his bookshelves, selecting a likely candidate and sitting himself down in an overstuffed chair to read it, page by page, for hours, as if nothing mattered more in all possible worlds than this action of carefully making ones way through this book.

＊

Jeff Goldblum attempting to play a piano underwater in the depths of a slow-flowing river while several people on dry land yell at him amicably to just give up. But he can't (or pretends he can't) hear them where he is. This is the nature of celebrity, he is thinking, as are some of the people on the bank.

＊

Jeff Goldblum, having given of himself, retreating quietly over the soft snow between the pines, going off into this forest, a tall lanky figure moving towards a large implacable red winter sun.

Acknowledgements

Huge thanks to Daniel Carpenter of The Paperchain Podcast for providing a place for me to vent the first variations on Jeff Goldblum, and for Gillian Best who gave me the prompt which started this all off. Thanks to Andrew Male for floating the perfect title down the Twitter stream. Thank you Heather McDaid and Laura Jones for the space to do this nonsense, and to my parents for everything. As always, I couldn't have survived this without Douglas Dunbar.

Biggest thanks are due to Jeff Goldblum himself, the real Jeff Goldblum, for living his inspirational self.

About Helen McClory

Helen McClory lives in Edinburgh and grew up between there and the Isle of Skye. Her debut novel, *Flesh of the Peach*, was published by Freight in Spring 2017. Her first collection, *On the Edges of Vision*, won the Saltire First Book of the Year 2015 and was republished by 404 Ink in Spring 2018. 404 Ink also published her newest collection *Mayhem & Death* in March 2018. There is a moor and a cold sea in her heart.